Tara was six.
"Can I have a party?" she asked.
"Yes," said Mum.

Tara sent cards to her friends.

Veejay came to the party.
He gave Tara a toy car.

Emma came to the party.
She gave Tara a scarf.

Martha came last.
She gave Tara one marble.

Then Martha put on the scarf.
"I want it," she said.

"It's Tara's scarf," said Emma.
Martha started to cry.

"Let's play Pass the Parcel," said Tara.
Tara passed the parcel to Veejay.

Veejay passed the parcel to Emma.

Emma passed the parcel to Martha.

Martha didn't pass the parcel.
She started to rip off all the paper.

"Pass the parcel!" said Tara.
Martha started to cry.
"I'm not playing," she said.

There were some sweets inside the parcel.
Veejay found them.

Martha started to cry again.
"I want the sweets," she said.

They had tea.
There were jam tarts and bananas.

"I'm starving," said Martha.
She ate ten jam tarts and five bananas.

"Let's play Hide and Seek," said Tara.

Veejay and Emma hid in the garden.
Tara found them.

Martha hid in the bath.
She found a lot of jars.
She took the lids off them.

Tara found Martha.
"Put the lids back on the jars," she said.

Martha started to cry again.

Emma's mum and Veejay's dad came for them.
"Was it a good party?" they asked.
"Yes," said Emma and Veejay.

Martha's mum came last.
"Was it a good party?" she asked.

"No," said Martha. "Everyone was nasty to me."